AN UNOFFICIAL GRAPHIC NOVEL
FOR MINECRAFTERS

SAVING XENOS

CARA J. STEVENS
ART BY WALKER MELBY

SCHOLASTIC INC.

ISBN 978-1-338-27720-3

12 11 10 9 8 7 6 5 4 3 2 1   18 19 20 21 22 23

Printed in the U.S.A.   40

First Scholastic printing, January 2018

Cover design by Brian Peterson
Cover illustration by Walker Melby

Many thanks to several talented Mine-imator creators for the use of their amazing rigs: Nimi, for 1.11 The Exploration Update rig pack; CraftinPark for the Book rig; EthanForeverAlone for the Mirror rig; SharkleSparkle for the Phone rig; and Josh the Stupad for the Welcome to California sign rig.

Designer: Joshua Barnaby
Interior layout: Nick Grant

INTRODUCTION

If you have played Minecraft, then you know all about Minecraft worlds. They're made of blocks you can mine: coal, dirt, and sand. In the game, you'll find many different creatures, lands, and villages inhabited by strange villagers with bald heads. The villagers who live there have their own special, magical worlds that are protected by a string of border worlds to stop outsiders from finding them.

Our story takes place on the small border world of Xenos. It is home to an assortment of villagers and miners who are learning to live peacefully with each other, as well as a family of pollinators who are entrusted with building new worlds, and a monastery filled with monks who ensure their safety.

When leaders of Xenos's main village turned Phoenix away for being a troublemaker, Phoenix, her family, and many of their friends settled outside the village walls. The nickname of their settlement, Phoenixtown, stuck, making Phoenix's family proud, but it made poor Phoenix uncomfortable every time she heard it.

We last left off as the evil Defender was exiled to a seed world, and life once again promised to be peaceful. Little did they know that the Defender left behind one last surprise: a glitch that could destroy all of Xenos and everyone in it forever.

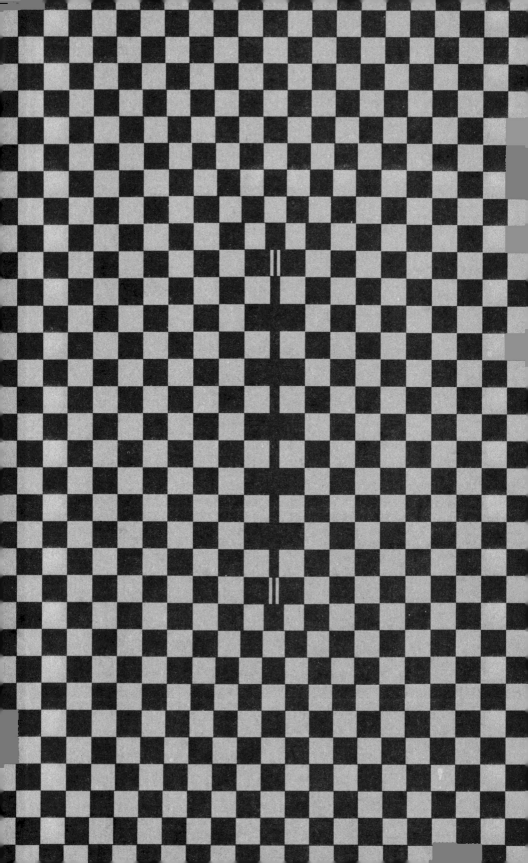

CHAPTER 1

HATCHING A PLAN

CLANG

CLANG

That never gets old!

lot to you, it esn't. Some of have sensitive ears.

We're off to the meeting. We'll tell you how it goes.

Good luck!

CRUNCH
CRUNCH CRUNCH

Whaa?

Busted! I have to get out of here!

What are you doing here?

PANT PANT

How about a little bet? If I can shoot an arrow closer to the bull's eye than she can, you tell us what you're up to.

That was the best Full Moon Festival ever! You and your family are real party animals, Wolfie!

You Villagers throw a great party! And now we're off to deliver those invitations of yours. Sniff ya' later, Phoenix.

These Olympic Games could be just the thing to unite all the people in this world.

I can't wait to see the looks on everyone's faces when they get the invitations.

What if the kids from Xenos can't come?

Wait... What if no one comes?

CHAPTER 2

THE FIRST
OLYMPICS

Kel felt bad about griefing us last Halloween, so he used his allowance to donate all the supplies for the games. Even the gold medals!
He must earn a lot for allowance! Sheesh!
You guys haven't stopped working all morning. Your mom sent me to tell you to take a break.
Good idea. I'm hungry! Did she send lunch for us or is that all for you?
I know I can be a pig sometimes, but I can't eat all this!
Thank goodness! I'm so hungry I could even eat mushroom stew!
Yuck! I'd rather eat an electrified Guardian than eat mushroom stew.

CHAPTER 3

FUNLAND

XENOS

LET THE GAMES BEGIN!

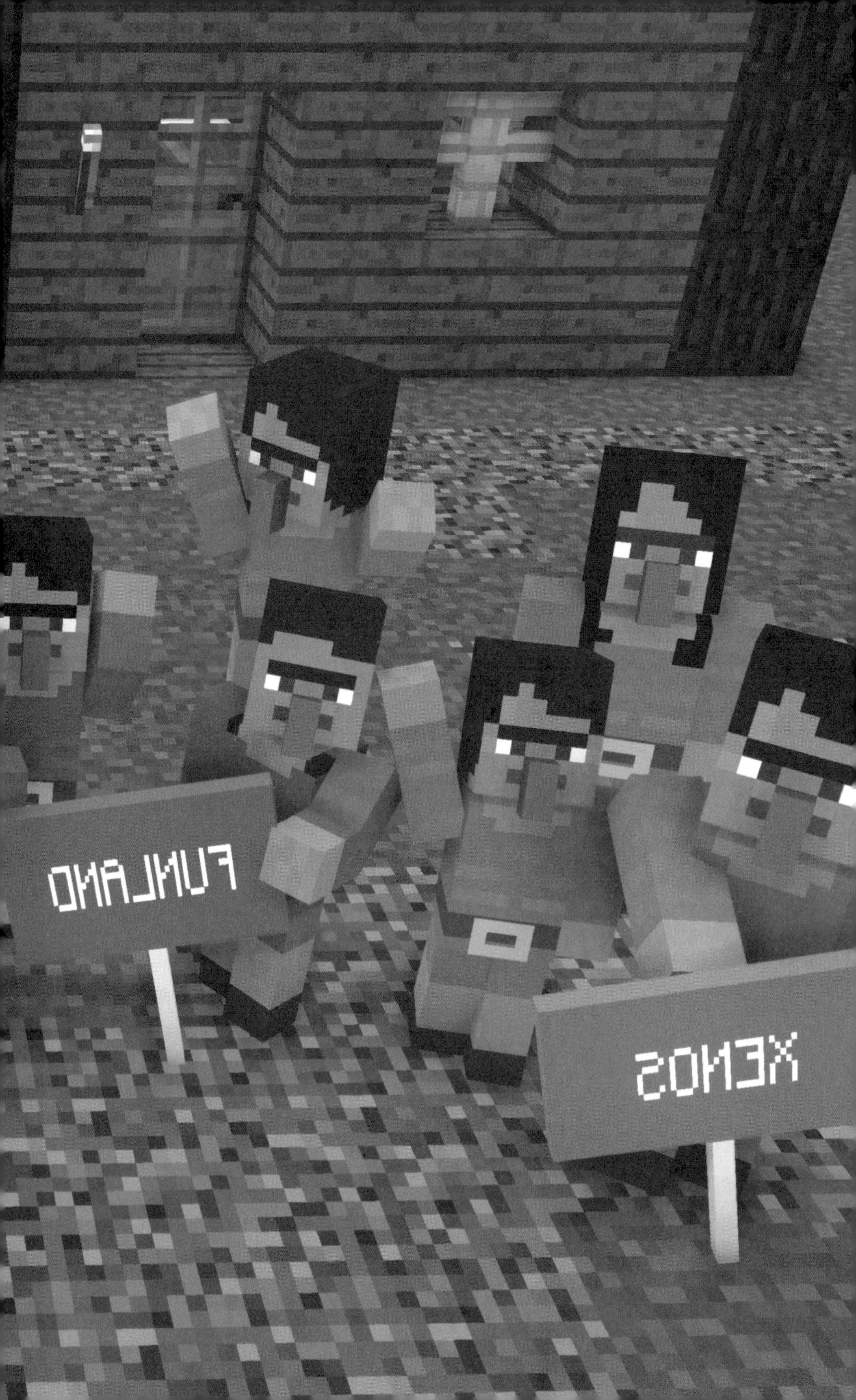

Look, Fracas! Archery is first! Nice!

Just a little higher, Fidget. There you go.

Thanks, T.H.!

Ooooooooooo!

We can't match their style points, but we shoot straight so we have a shot!

CHAPTER 4

DIRE WARNING

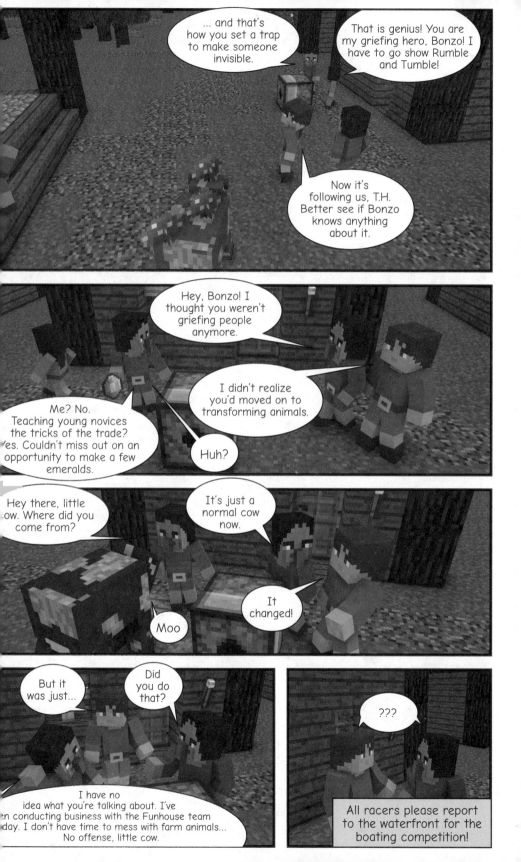

CHAPTER 5

A SECRET MISSION

Here are some more supplies.
That was some quick thinking, by the way, coming up with that fib about the Olympic committee. I'm sorry it made you look foolish...

I don't mind. Someone recently reminded me that I've gotten a kind of a big head with all this Prophetess thing. My reputation could use a little tarnishing.

I should go tell Ole Baba... I mean Bailey – I keep forgetting she goes by Bailey now... and Leila. They may have some advice for us.
And some potions, too.

CHAPTER 6

ZOMBIES
IN THE NIGHT

CHAPTER 7

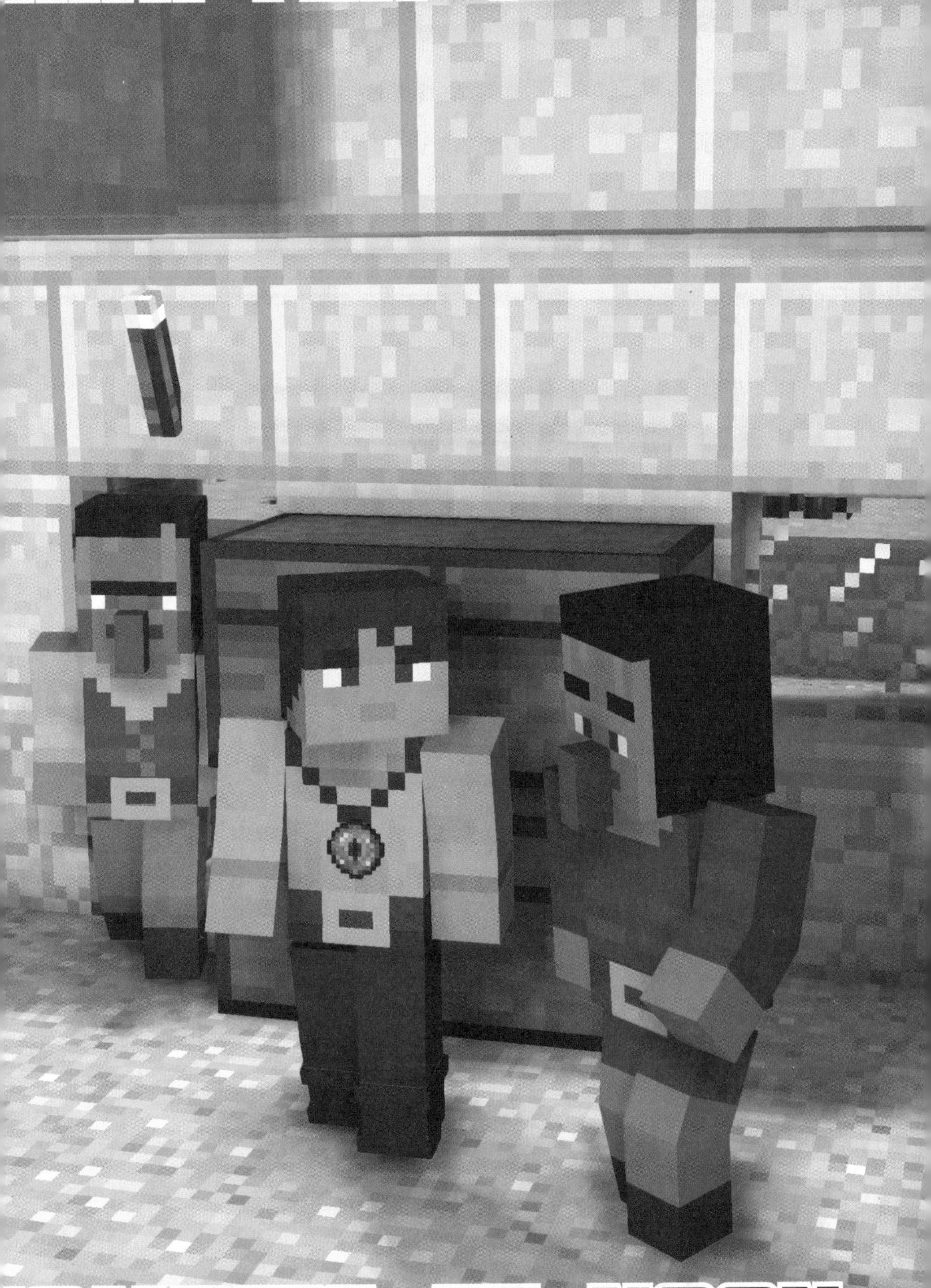

ZOMBIES AT NOON

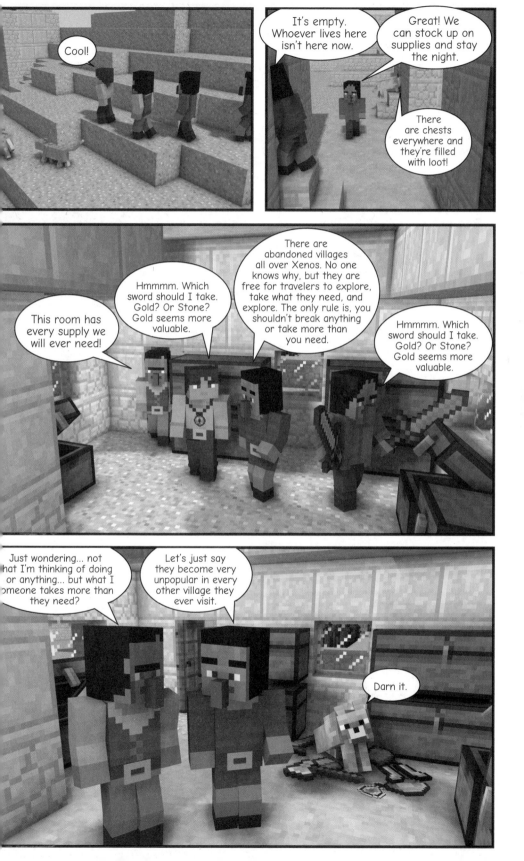

You found something to read? Good for you, Phoenix. You're finally picking up a...

SLAM!

SPLA

Oh. That makes more sense

Don't stay up too late reading. You need to get a good night's sleep!

CHAPTER 8

LLAGERS

CHAPTER 9

THE GLITCH

What do you know about the Far Lands, Brandor?

My grandfather claims he once went to the Far Lands. When I was little, told stories to scare me i following the rules.

What kinds of stories?

Like one about a guy who tricked his brother and stole his pe ocelot. He got sent to the Lands and was never hea from again.

Or the one about the girl who lied to her mother so she got sent to the Far Lands and was never heard from again.

Or the one about the kid who didn't eat his vegetables and...

Let me guess, he got sent to the Far Lands and was never heard from again?

No, actually he was forced to work on a farm to know the value of a hard day's work. They weren't all about the Far Lands, come to think of it.

They're more experienced with world building. And they're all grownups! We're just a bunch of kids.
And a dog and a cat. We're important, too.
The monks can sense that something is wrong, but they can't fix it. My parents, the pollinators, can turn worlds on and shut them off, but they can't fix anything either.
We've proven that through all our adventures, we are good at fixing things!
Just think, Xander: If we can fix this world, maybe we can fix others, too. Maybe oth worlds won't have to be turned off.

CHAPTER 10

ATTACK OF THE KILLER COOKIES

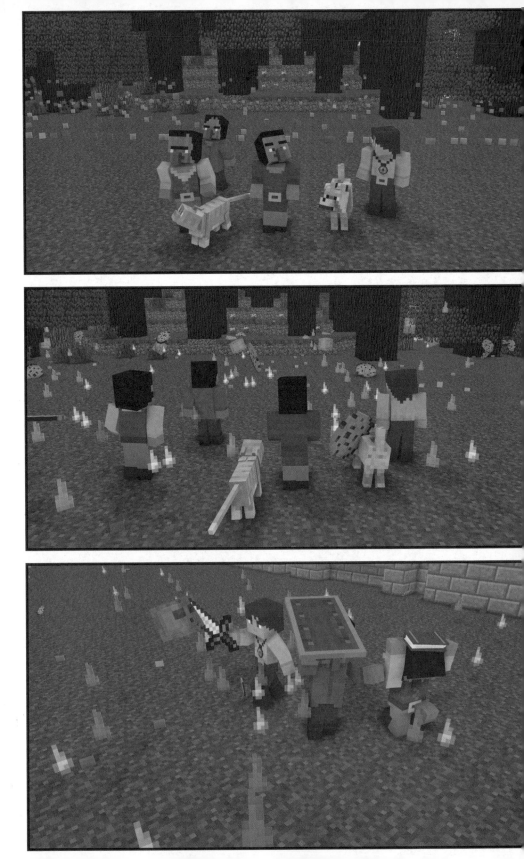

CHAPTER 11

THE TOWER

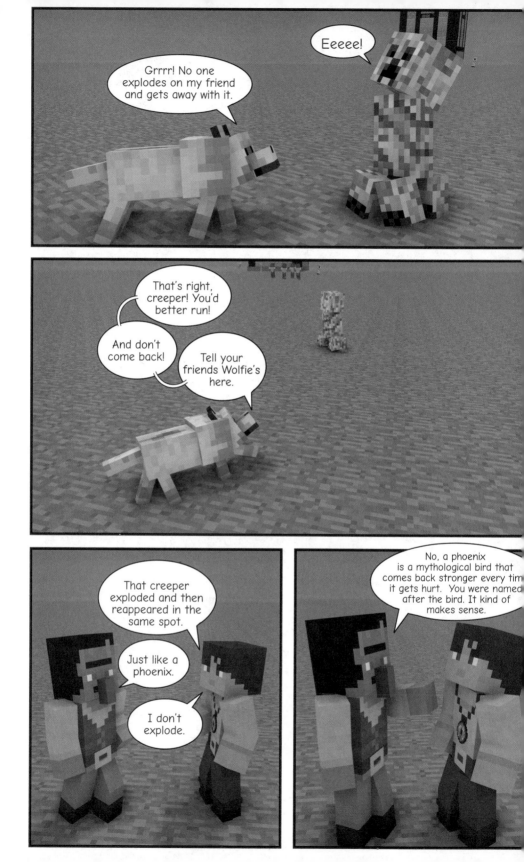

You came back after the witch turned your brother into a zombie, and after the monks were also turned into zombies. You even turned the witch back into Leila and returned her to her sister.
And you kept coming back after the Defender. He definitely didn't count on how persistent you would be to make sure he never hurt anyone again.

We all came back after him. I couldn't have done any of it without you guys. And now we're here to finish the job! So let's get to that tower!

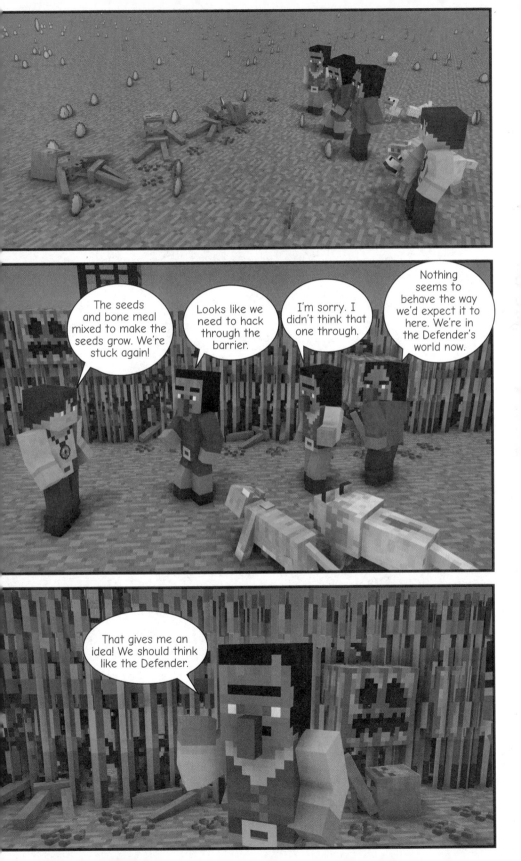

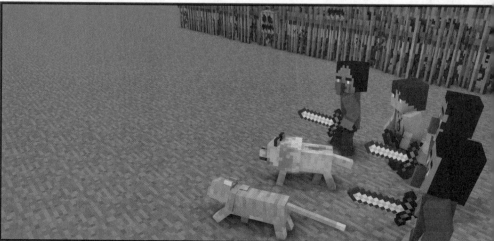

CHAPTER 12

MAGIC MIRROR

A pressure plate. I'll have this deactivated in a nano-second.

Why are you complaining? You can take a nap and teleport to Phoenix when she reaches the top.

Hey, Brandor! Can you make a redstone machine that will help us climb this stupid tower?

CHAPTER 13

OMECOMING

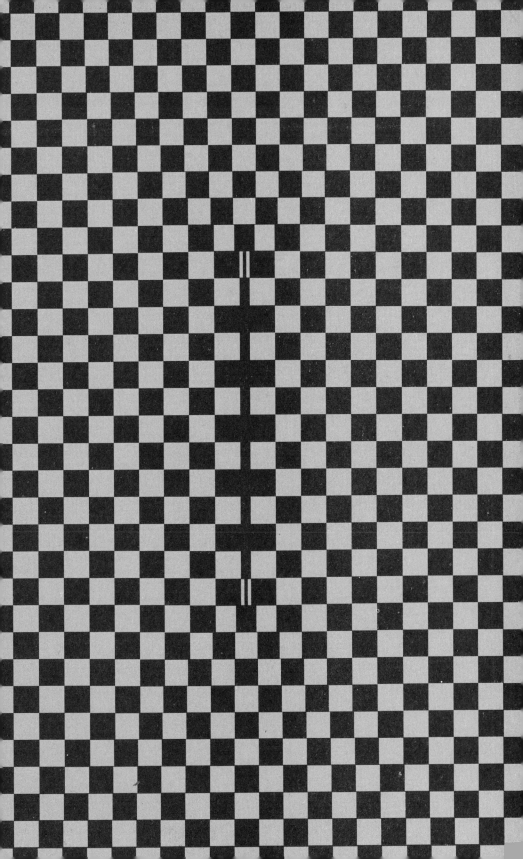

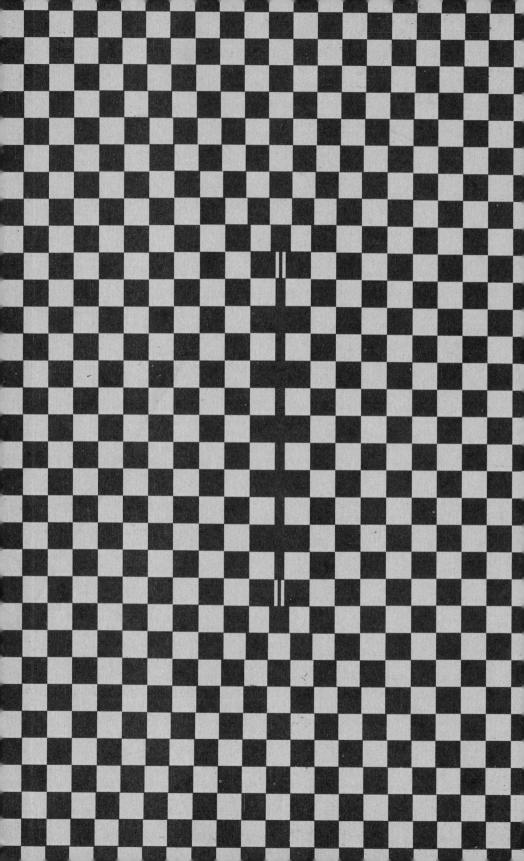